Bad Bert in Trouble

story by Jeremy Strong

illustrated by Steve Smallman

Mouse, Jojo, Sam and Ben were
playing by the stream.
"Look out," said Jojo.
"Here comes Grumpyboots."

Grumpyboots looked at
the children.
"You must not play there,"
he said. "You might fall in."

"I fell in when I was six," said Sam.

"Brave Mouse saved me."

Mouse felt proud.

He looked at the scar on his arm.

The children went to climb the trees.
"Here comes Grumpyboots again,"
said Ben.
"You must not climb the trees,"
said Grumpyboots. "You might fall out."

"I fell out when I was six," said Sam.
"I was trying to save Bad Bert."
"Bad Bert is a bad cat,"
said Grumpyboots, "and he does not
belong to anybody."

"I am fed up with Grumpyboots,"
said Ben. "Let's go to the secret room."

The secret room was dark and
cool and quiet.
Then Mouse heard a low noise.

"What is that?" he said.

Mouse was scared.

His eyes got bigger and bigger.

"What is it?" asked Jojo.
Ben began to look round
the room carefully.

Grrrrrrrr

Ben shone the torch into the corner.

"It is Bad Bert," he said.

"I think he is ill."

Bad Bert was curled up.

There was dry blood on his fur.

He growled at them. "Grrrrrr."

"Bad Bert needs help," said Ben.

"Our mum will help," said Jojo.

"We have a box at home that we can carry him in."

Mouse and Jojo ran home to get the box.

When they got back to the
secret room Sam was stroking the cat.
"You are going to be all right,"
she said softly.
"Grrrrrr," growled Bad Bert.

"Lift him carefully," said Ben.

Mouse opened the box.

Jojo and Sam put Bad Bert inside.

"Grrrrrr," grumbled Bad Bert.

The children took Bad Bert to the
twins' house.
"Mum will be home soon," Jojo said.
"She will know what to do."
Mouse gave Bad Bert some water,
but the cat did not want it.

The twins' mum was worried when she
saw the cat.
"I think he has been hit by a car,"
she said.

"Will he be all right?" asked the children.
"I don't know," said Mrs Macdonald.
"He looks very ill. We must take him
to the vet."

The vet looked at Bad Bert.
"He has been hit by a car,"
he said.

"Sometimes animals can be badly
hurt inside. I don't know if he will live.
I will keep him here."
"Grrrrrrrrr," growled Bad Bert.
"I wish I could look after him," said Sam.
"I do hope he will be all right."

The next day the children went back
to the vet.
They were worried.
They thought Bad Bert might have died
in the night.

"Bad Bert is sleeping,"
said the vet. "I am looking after him.
Now we will just have to wait."

When the children got back to the twins'
house someone was waiting to see them.
"It's Grumpyboots!" cried Sam.
"His name is Mr Green,"
laughed Mrs Macdonald.
"Someone told me Bad Bert was very ill,"
said Mr Green. "Is he all right?"

"But you don't like Bad Bert," said Sam.
"I don't like stray cats," said Mr Green,
"but I don't want them to be hurt.
I do hope Bad Bert will be all right."
"He is with the vet and he is getting
better," said Mrs Macdonald.
"Thank you for asking after him."

Five days went by.
Bad Bert got better and better.

Then the vet said that Bad Bert
could go home.
The children put him in the box.
They took him back to the park.

Prrrrrrrrrr